Mum and Dad were
spring-cleaning.

1

Mum looked in a drawer.

Dad threw things out.

The children looked at the junk.

They played with the old toys.

Mum put the old toys in the car.

The children were sad.

They all went to the jumble sale.

JUMBLE
SALE

DOORS
OPEN
AT
10 O'CLOCK

The children wanted to buy something.

"What a lot of junk!" said Wilf.

The children saw their toys.

They counted their money.

It was time to go home.

"What's in the bags?" said Mum.

Oh no!